Freedom Technique

by

JOAN LAST

Book 3

These technical exercises, designed to follow those in Books 1 and 2, cover a fairly wide range of grades approximately from V upwards. They are primarily for those whose time is limited, but could be of use to more serious students needing to overcome certain weaknesses.

The material here presented should serve to bridge the gap between the easier studies and exercises available for early-grade pupils and the more formidable books written for performing pianists.

The student should always be alive to the technical problems that appear in the music he is studying, and this alertness, coupled with imagination and initiative, will enable him to improvise many sequences other than those included in this book.

J.L.

TECHNICAL HINTS

Sit easily not too close to the Keyboard, sit towards the front of the stool so that the body is not rigid or unable to move sideways. The ideal height is that which allows the arm to be level from elbow to wrist (but many renowned pianists sit at different heights).

Never allow tension in the hands. Avoid constant pressure into the keys or "pulling in" of the knuckles. Let the fingers be curved but not unduly bent or lifted high after striking the key. In this way playing becomes a natural, easy action.

The last finger joint makes direct contact with the key, therefore it should always be in a condition of awareness and exertion.

In fast playing make sure the arm is light and does not bear down on the fingers. Its function is to *support* the hand and carry it up and down the keyboard when speed is required.

Arm Weight, used for warmer touch in melody or chord, comes from the forearm, which is relaxed. This weight is conveyed to the finger-tips via the wrist. The wrist controls the amount of weight given to the keys by the amount of flexibility used. A rigid wrist will cause hard touch, a flabby wrist dull, thin tone.

In *Staccato* avoid any imposed upward movement. Strike the key from above the surface with added speed and the upward movement is the natural rebound. Again, avoid a flabby wrist.

Rotary movement entails a slight swing towards the 5th finger by "rolling" the Rotary muscles in the forearm. It relieves tension in Broken Octaves, Alberti bass and many other passages. These muscles need to be in a condition of freedom (even if not visibly "rolling") in all playing except Octave passages or Martellato chords.

The Lateral muscles allow the arm to swing sideways and their freedom is essential in Arpeggio passages, widespread Broken chords or at any moment when the keyboard has to be covered over a wide area. It is the Arm that carries and supports the hands and fingers allowing them to be in a constant condition of freedom.

Therefore avoid muscular tension at all times and Piano playing will lose the sense of effort which was apparent in the Technique of 50 years ago.

All the Exercises in "Freedom Technique" are designed to promote an easy and natural Technique and I hope the student will find them helpful towards this end.

For the Performing Artist more rigorous tests will be needed, but will only be accomplished if *Freedom* has been achieved in earlier stages.

Joan Last

Oxford University Press

Music Department, 37 Dover Street, London W1X 4AH

ARM WEIGHT AND FIRM FINGERS, ALTERNATING WITH QUICK LIGHT STACCATO

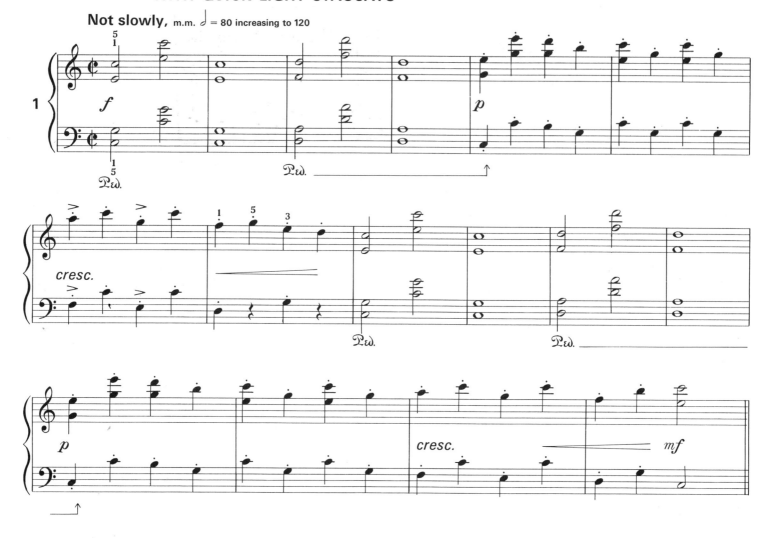

ROTATION, ALTERNATING WITH FIVE-FINGER GROUPS

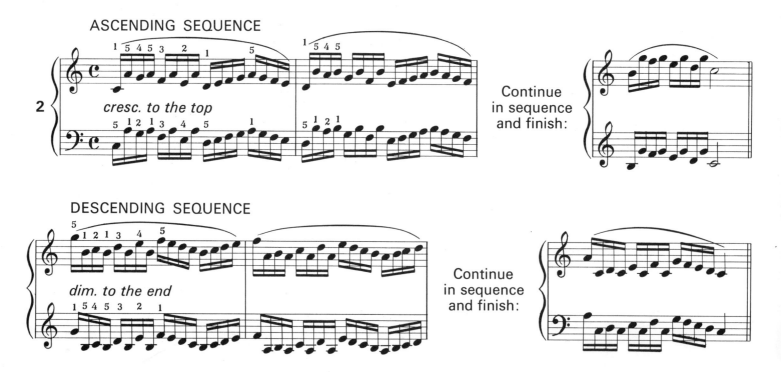

SCALE SEQUENCE WITH CRESCENDO AND DIMINUENDO

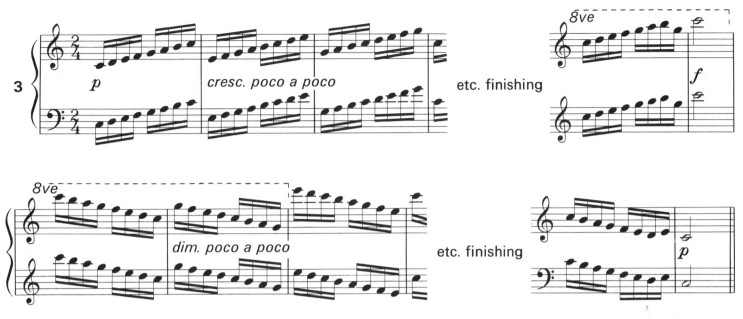

3 *p*   *cresc. poco a poco*   etc. finishing   *f*

dim. poco a poco   etc. finishing   *p*

As an Introductory Exercise to the above, practise each section within the bar separately

e.g.

FURTHER KEYS should be played with suitable fingering

WIDE SKIPS—STACCATO AND SLURS—FAST TEMPO, WITH LIGHT ARM
IN ALL KEYS

R.H. fingering above
L.H. fingering below
RIGHT HAND

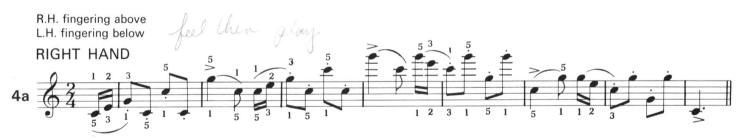

4a

4b LEFT HAND plays above exercise, starting 2 octaves lower.

WIDER SKIPS

RIGHT HAND

5a

5b LEFT HAND plays above exercise, starting 2 octaves lower.

Freedom technique Book 3

LATERAL MOVEMENT FOR SMOOTH THUMB TURN IN ARPEGGIOS
IN ALL KEYS, WITH APPROPRIATE FINGERING

RIGHT HAND *Legato* and *Staccato*

LEFT HAND

DOUBLE 3rds

Accents only light at first and increasing in intensity with the *crescendo*.

Freedom technique Book 3

CONTRACTIONS AND EXPANSIONS

RIGHT HAND

8a

LEFT HAND

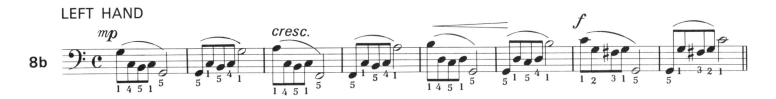

8b

RIGHT HAND

9a

LEFT HAND

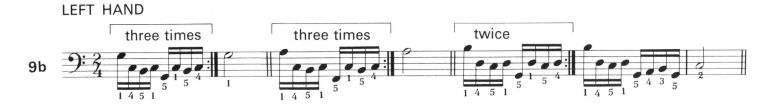

9b

ROTATION EXTENDING TO OCTAVE
IN ALL KEYS

SEPARATELY OR TOGETHER

10

EXERTION ON ACCENTS—RELEASE OF EXERTION (LIGHT ARM) ON SEMIQUAVERS

11

CHORD SEQUENCE FOR FULL TONE AND PEDAL CHANGES
EASY ARM WEIGHT AND FIRM LAST FINGER JOINT

12b Repeat above Chord Sequence over 4 octaves, quickly and lightly without pedal.

CHROMATIC AND DIATONIC SEQUENCES
WITH TRIPLET—DUPLET RHYTHM
TO BE REPEATED IN VARIOUS KEYS.
Play with *crescendo* or *diminuendo*, *legato* or *staccato*. (2nd sequence from D flat, etc.)

RIGHT HAND

13b It will be found more practical to start the LEFT HAND sequences from the top of the scale.

QUICKNESS AND ACCURACY IN CROSSING HANDS
REPEAT IN ALL KEYS

Quick and light, use 3rd finger throughout.

ROTATION–WITH FIVE-FINGER GROUPS IN ALL KEYS
(TRANSPOSING EXERCISE)

Same fingering throughout. Increase speed to *Presto.*

15

etc. finishing

BROKEN OCTAVES ALTERNATING WITH SCALES

Introductory Exercise.

etc., in sequence

To be played with separate hands at first.
ASCENDING SEQUENCE (white keys only)

16

etc. finishing

DESCENDING SEQUENCE (with Introductory Exercise Inverted)

etc. finishing

ARPEGGIO SEQUENCE FOR ALL KEYS (MAJOR AND MINOR)
LATERAL FREEDOM FOR *LEGATO* GROUPS UP TO m.m. ♩=92
FREE MOVEMENT ACROSS KEYS FOR ARPEGGIOS AT SPEED

SEPARATELY OR TOGETHER

For the above exercise use standard (root position) fingering in each key:
for example, key D flat maj. begins thus:

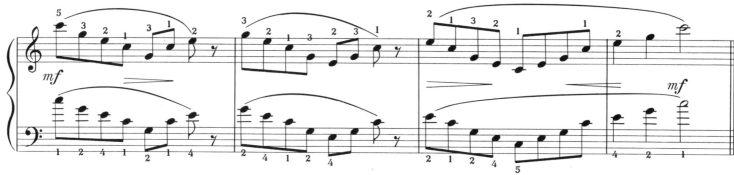

SLURS—ALTERNATING TENSION AND RELEASE OF WEIGHT

TO BE PLAYED IN VARIOUS KEYS with suitable finger changes.

RIGHT HAND

LEFT HAND

Freedom technique Book 3

RHYTHMIC GROUPINGS
Keep a metronomic beat.

m.m. between ♩ = 80 and ♩ = 132

RIGHT HAND

19

LEFT HAND works downwards from Middle C.

Play the above exercise hands separately and in various keys. Remember that the lighter the arm, the faster the fingers can move. Always observe correct scale fingering.

Enjoyment can be added to scale practise if various rhythms are attempted:

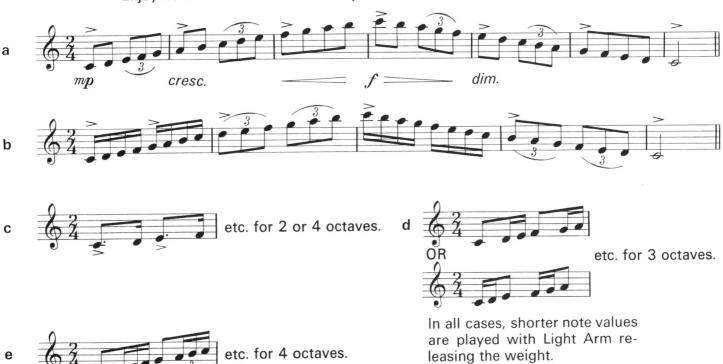

a   *mp*   *cresc.*   *f*   *dim.*

b

c   etc. for 2 or 4 octaves.   d   etc. for 3 octaves.

OR

In all cases, shorter note values are played with Light Arm releasing the weight.

e   etc. for 4 octaves.

PATTERN FOR CHROMATIC PRACTICE
Start in either hand, on any note.

R.H. fingering above
L.H. fingering below

20

Freedom technique Book 3

CHORD SEQUENCE
For arm weight with firm fingers, and clean pedal changes for each chord.

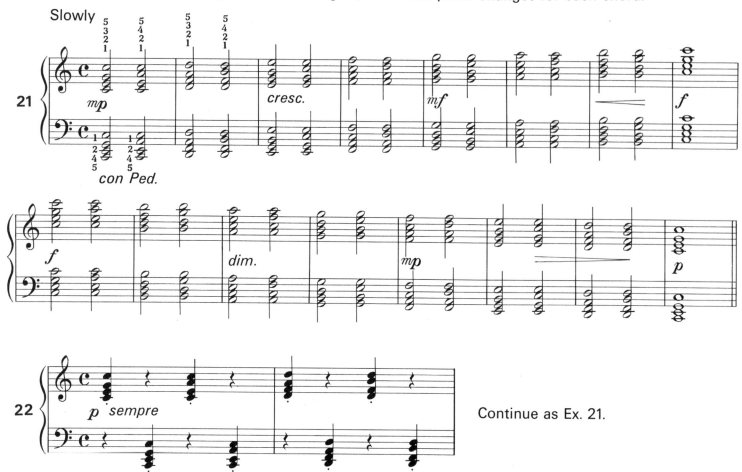

21 Slowly
mp
con Ped.
cresc.
mf
f
f
dim.
mp
p

22
p sempre
Continue as Ex. 21.

RIGHT HAND ALONE (*legato* and *staccato*).

23 Continue as Ex. 21.

LEFT HAND plays 2 octaves lower.

FOR EXACT MATCHING OF TONE IN ARPEGGIO RUNS

ASCENDING SEQUENCE Every note even

24
(No pedal)

Continue in above chord sequence as Ex. 21

DESCENDING SEQUENCE

Continue in descending sequence

REPEATED NOTES

RIGHT HAND

etc. finishing

LEFT HAND

etc. finishing

FIRM 5th FINGER IN OCTAVE EXPANSIONS

RIGHT HAND

LEFT HAND

LIGHT ARM, TRAVELLING QUICKLY OVER THE KEYBOARD

RIGHT HAND

27b LEFT HAND as above, starting one octave lower.
Fingering pattern: 5 1 2 3 4 ascending
1 5 2 3 4 descending

QUICK EXTENSIONS AND CONTRACTIONS
FOR SUPPLE HAND AND THUMB

Continue up the piano,
finishing on C.

LEFT HAND MOVES DOWNWARDS (Chromatically)

Continue down, finishing on C.

Freedom technique Book 3

THIRDS WITH STACCATO AND CROSSING HANDS

ASCENDING SEQUENCE

29a

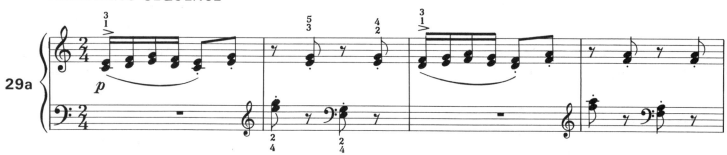

Continue upwards, finishing:

DESCENDING SEQUENCE

ending:

ASCENDING SEQUENCE

29b

ending:

DESCENDING SEQUENCE

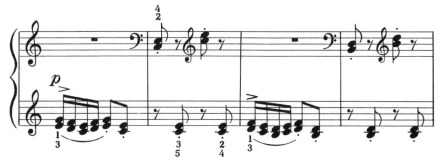

ending:

Freedom technique Book 3

BROKEN CHORD SEQUENCES FOR LATERAL EASE

Separately at first. Listen for eveness. Practise first with accent on 1st beat—
then with accent on 2nd beat.

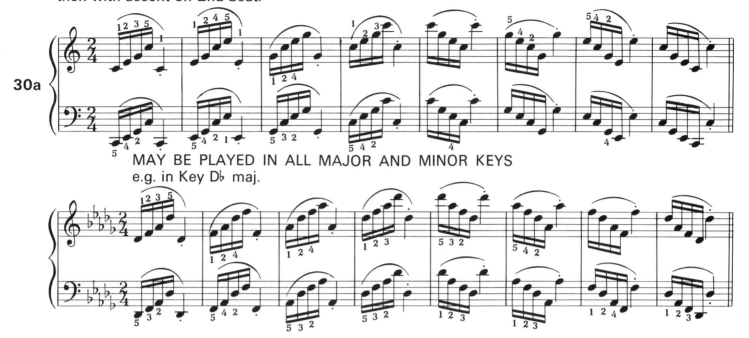

30a

MAY BE PLAYED IN ALL MAJOR AND MINOR KEYS
e.g. in Key D♭ maj.

Practice of above groups may be extended as follows:

30b

etc.

31 Repeat Exercise 30a and b
with this chord formation:

etc.

LIGHT ARM AND EASY MOVEMENT ACROSS KEYBOARD IN ARPEGGIOS
Count 2, maintain a metronomic beat

m.m. ♩ = 80 rising to ♩ = 132

32

Repeat in each hand separately and in all keys.

FOR EXERTING AND RELEASING WEIGHT
Release weight by lightening arm on semiquavers.

RIGHT HAND

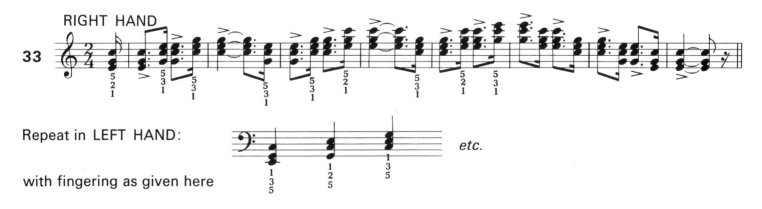

33

Repeat in LEFT HAND:

etc.

with fingering as given here

Freedom technique Book 3

HELD VOICES

RIGHT HAND—*LEGATO* CROTCHETS—LIGHT ACCOMPANYING SEMIQUAVERS

LEFT HAND plays above exercise with this finger pattern:
Ascending ⑤ 2 1 2 ④ 2 1 2   Descending ① 4 5 4 ② 4 5 4

FINGER CHANGES

RIGHT HAND

LEFT HAND

RIGHT HAND   LEFT HAND

FINGERS PASSING OBLIQUELY OVER

RIGHT HAND *(legato)*   LEFT HAND *(legato)*

SLIDING THE THUMB AND PASSING 4th OVER 5th

RIGHT HAND *(legato)*

LEFT HAND *(legato)*

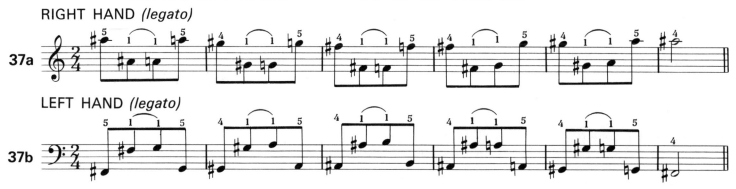

PREPARATION FOR TRILLS

Observe the fingering.
Finger touch — no weight from the arm. Ensure Rotary Freedom.
RIGHT HAND

LEFT HAND plays descending group of trills, using same finger sequence
as right hand:

NEATNESS IN TURNS (1)

RIGHT HAND

LEFT HAND

NEATNESS IN TURNS (2)

Lighten the arm for the quick notes.
RIGHT HAND

LEFT HAND

Also practise Exx. 40a and 40b in this rhythm.   *etc.*

LATERAL SWING

RIGHT HAND

41a

LEFT HAND

41b

SPREAD CHORDS—LEGATO OR STACCATO

RIGHT HAND *(slowly)*   LEFT HAND

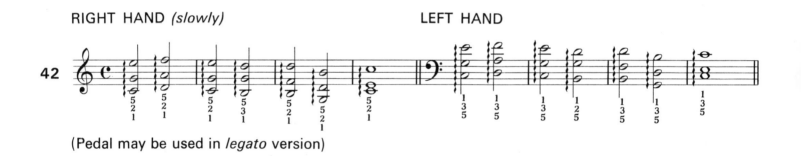

42

(Pedal may be used in *legato* version)

TWO VOICES—STACCATO AND LEGATO—IN ONE HAND

RIGHT HAND ALONE   *legato*

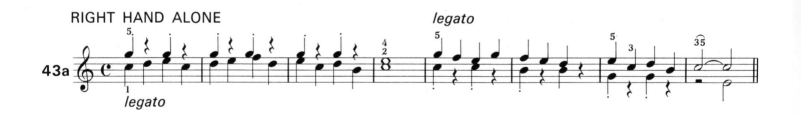

43a

legato

LEFT HAND ALONE

legato

43b

legato

Freedom technique Book 3

CHORD SEQUENCE AND VARIATIONS—MAY BE USED ASCENDING OR DESCENDING

Observe the fingering and use *legato* pedalling.

RIGHT HAND   LEFT HAND

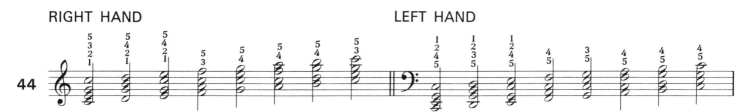

Descending version uses the same fingering.

RIGHT HAND—up only

Continue, using chord sequence.

LEFT HAND—down only

Continue, using descending sequence.

RIGHT HAND

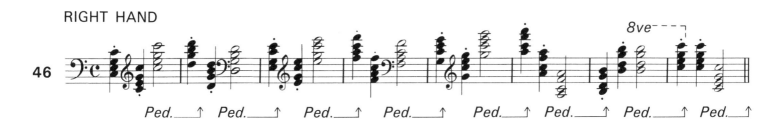

Repeat Ex. 46 in LEFT HAND, starting 2 octaves lower.

RIGHT HAND

Repeat Ex. 47 in the LEFT HAND, using fingering of Ex. 44.

Freedom technique Book 3

SCALES AND CHANGE OF DIRECTION IN ALTERNATE HANDS

TO BE PLAYED IN ALL KEYS.

FURTHER ARPEGGIO PRACTICE — INCLUDING INVERSIONS

RIGHT HAND

LEFT HAND

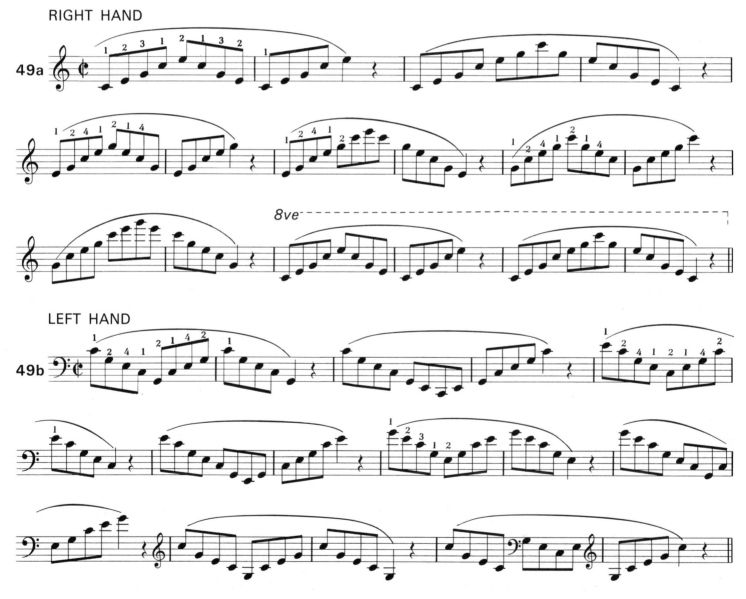

Exx. 49a and 49b may be played in all keys, using standard arpeggio fingering.
Also practise *staccato*.

TWO AGAINST THREE
(CROSS TIME)

Now practise 2-octave scales 2 against 3. When the left hand plays the triplet start 2 octaves lower than right hand.

PREPARATION FOR SCALES IN 3rds

EACH BAR FIRST *STACCATO* AND REPEAT *LEGATO*—OBSERVE FINGERING EXACTLY

RIGHT HAND (SLOWLY AT FIRST)

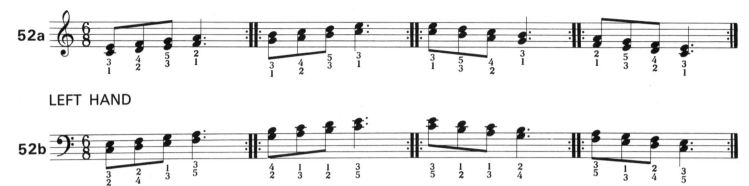

LEFT HAND

The above fingering applies to keys C, G, D, A, major and minor, from which the complete scale may be played extending the number of octaves.

FOR FLEXIBLE TURNS

After preliminary practice omit bracketed bars 3 and 8 in both 53a and 53b.

RIGHT HAND

LEFT HAND

EVEN TONE IN SEQUENCE OF 6ths AND 3rds

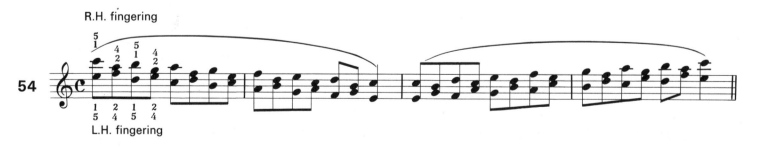

LEFT HAND An octave lower

Play the above exercise *legato* and *staccato*, and in slurred pairs

CHROMATIC SCALES WITH 'OBLIQUE' FINGERING AND DIMINISHED 7ths

R.H. fingering above
L.H. fingering below

etc.—continue chromatically in each hand, ascending. L.H. starts an octave lower.

DESCENDING VERSION:

etc.—in sequence.

SIMPLE PATTERNS FOR PLAYING DOMINANT 7th ARPEGGIOS, FOLLOWED BY MAJOR OR MINOR ARPEGGIOS

Key C (in either hand)

MORE DIFFICULT DOMINANT 7th GROUPS—INCLUDING INVERSIONS

ALL KEYS

CHROMATIC 3rds

Each group to be played several times — alternately *legato* and *staccato*

RIGHT HAND

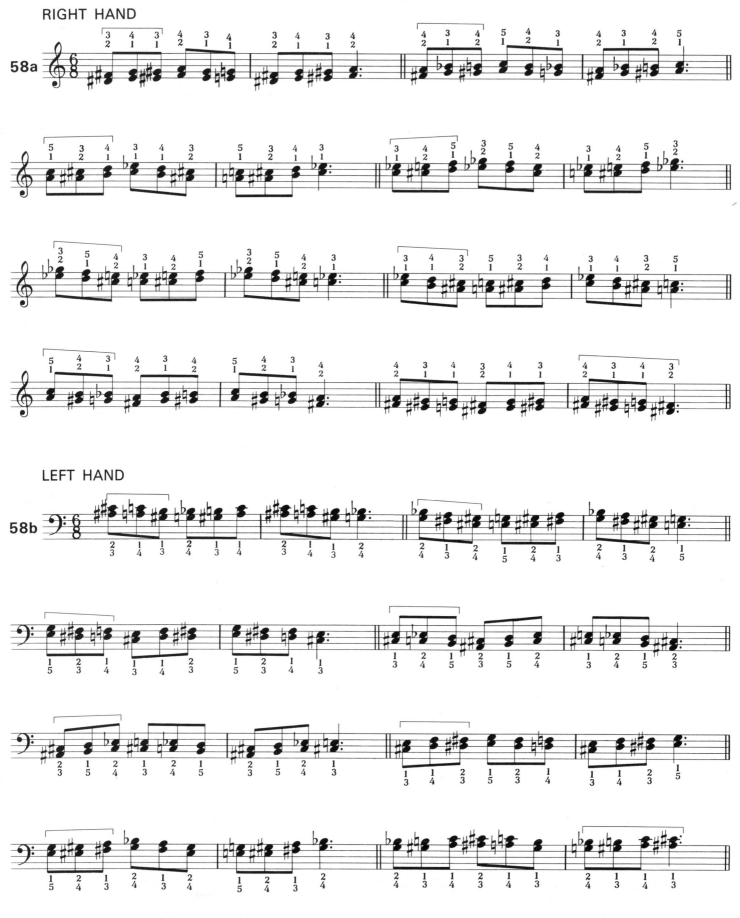

LEFT HAND

Exx. 58a and 58b may be played together with identical fingering in contrary motion. Follow with complete scales in chromatic 3rds by playing continuously the groups marked ⌐——⌐.

OCTAVES

Keep close to the keys—wrist flexible but not flabby.
Do not rest on the octave before striking it.
Sequences for all keys.

In all keys.

Continue in sequence. Ex. 60 may be played at a quicker speed and in this rhythm:

Follow Exx. 59—60 with
double-octave scales in
all keys—3 8ve compass.

DIMINISHED 7th GROUPS

Hands separately at first.

When the above exercise can be played with ease the sequence should be played in a continuous quaver rhythm.

etc. (Again hands separately at first.)

CHROMATIC OCTAVES

Legato or *Staccato,* or in slurred pairs, using 4th finger where possible, on black keys.

ASCENDING SEQUENCE

Continue up in sequence, starting chromatic scale on white keys only (next one D) and descending on all white keys.

DESCENDING SEQUENCE

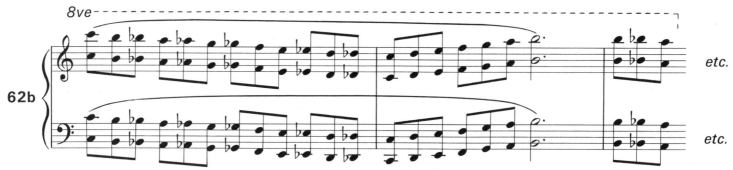

etc.

etc.

All the exercises in this book are representative of many more that can be improvised by the student who meets with technical problems in the music that he plays.

Freedom technique Book 3

Processed and printed by
Halstan & Co. Ltd., Amersham, Bucks., England